REAL
Christianity

INDIVIDUAL AND SMALL GROUP
STUDY GUIDE

DALE PARTRIDGE

RELEARN PRESS

Table of Contents

How to Use This Study Guide

The *Real Christianity* study guide is designed to be experienced in a group setting such as a Bible study, community group, or home church. That said, it can absolutely be used for individuals as well.

The study guide experience is broken into eight sessions correlating with each chapter. Sessions can be completed in a one-per-week or two-per-week format. Sessions should be possible to complete within 60-90 minutes or in approximately 30 minutes for individuals.

For those in a church setting, in order to assure everyone has enough time to participate in discussions, it is recommended that large groups break up into smaller groups of four to six people. We suggest every group appoint a facilitator who has both read the book and feels gifted and responsible for leading the discussion and facilitating an orderly and fruitful conversation.

From our personal experience, we suggest each group appoints a host (who could also be the facilitator) who is responsible for creating a comfortable and organized environment, snacks and drinks, or even a meal prior to your session.

WEEKLY PREPARATION

Each participant should have their own copy of the *Real Christianity* book and study guide, which includes notes for each session and directions for activities and discussion questions. In preparation for each session, participants should complete the corresponding chapter in the *Real Christianity* book.

PRACTICAL EXPECTATIONS

To reach the spiritual goals set for the next four-to-eight weeks (depending on your group's pace), we encourage all participants to discipline themselves to view the study guide content through the lens of Scripture and not through their emotions or personal experience. Ultimately, any discussion should be biblical, edifying and fruitful to the members of the group.

SUGGESTED GATHERING STRUCTURE

Meetings should be opened by the facilitator with a welcome sentiment, confirmation that each member has read the material, brief announcements, and prayer. Each session includes an introduction (to be read by the facilitator) as a way to set the stage for the upcoming group discussion, a brief scripture reflection, and a series of questions. Consider closing the meeting with group prayer and reminding members of the upcoming chapters to be completed.

"Tell the men of the world, and, let them see by your example and spirit, that Christianity is not the gloomy thing they imagine—that a life of holiness is a life of real happiness."

JOHN MACDUFF

Getting Real About Real Christianity

Dear Christian, It takes a mature believer to set aside the daily demands of life and carve out time to carefully examine your personal walk with Jesus. As you go through this study guide, remember that your relationship with God has already been paid for on the cross. Put away your wallet and step off the stage—you can't buy any more love or earn any more affection from your Heavenly Father—you've already got it all. The *Real Christianity* experience is grasped not by doing more or being better, but by submitting and resting in the sufficient work of Christ.

As you work through this book, I pray you will do so with humility and submission to the Scriptures. While God is looking for a practical relationship that incorporates the theological elements of His character, He is most interested in your devotional relationship with His Son. It is here where we can find a deep understanding of who we are as Christians.

Dale Partridge,
Bend, Oregon July 2019

Belief In Christ Doesn't Make You Christian

INTRODUCTION *(read as a group)*

Let's talk about relationship. How do you know if you're close to someone? The answer should be obvious. If you're close with someone, you find yourself thinking about them. You go out of your way to spend time with them. You prioritize your life so that you can be with them—even if there's no agenda. And while we might have that kind of relationship with our spouse or children, many struggle to have that kind of relationship with God. Relationship with God, however, is simply an extension of our salvation through Christ. For this reason, our ground for relationship is best understood through our knowledge of salvation.

SCRIPTURE REFLECTION *(read as a group)*

> *"If you confess with your mouth the Lord Jesus and believe in your heart that God has raised Him from the*

dead, you will be saved. For with the heart one believes unto righteousness, and with the mouth confession is made unto salvation." **–ROMANS 10:9-10**

This passage written by the Apostle Paul can often feel like salvation is too simple. But as the book unpacked in this week's reading, salvation requires three things: (1) Belief that Jesus is the Christ, (2) a willingness to make Him Lord, and (3) a recognition that God raised Jesus from the dead. It's through these three postures which God initiates both deliverance from sin and its consequences and restores us into right relationship with Himself (a.k.a salvation).

GROUP DISCUSSION *(discuss as a group)*

01. How long have you been a Christian? How did you view salvation when you first came to Christ? Do you believe Christ saved you and then taught you these biblical truths or were these truths presented to you at your conversion?

02. What do you think the Apostle means by, "For with the heart one believes unto righteousness, and with the mouth confession is made unto salvation"? Is this an explanation of what happens to a new believer or are these required action steps for establishing your faith? Discuss.

03. Why is a recognition of the resurrection so critical for a salvation in Christ? Is it possible to believe in Jesus without the resurrection? Is the Gospel true without the resurrection? Read 1 Corinthians 15:1-33 and discuss your findings.

"The nature of Christ's salvation is woefully misrepresented by the modern evangelist. He announces a Savior from hell rather than a Savior from sin. That is why so many are fatally deceived, they wish to escape the Lake of Fire but not to be delivered from their sin."

A.W. PINK

If Some are False Then None is True

INTRODUCTION *(read as a group)*

Western culture caters to self. If the Western Church could chant it would say, "We are the consumer and it's all about us!" Unfortunately, what often happens is a blending of this cultural coddling into our spiritual life with God and His Word. That is to say, we end up expecting the Bible to be about us. However, Scripture is not about us. It's for us. But it's about Christ.

In fact, every single story in Scripture is either preparing us for or pointing us to Jesus. When we realize that David and Goliath is not about us and *our* giants and how Abraham is not about us and *our* faith and how the lions of Daniel are not about us and *our* enemies, we can finally begin to see who these stories are truly about.

SCRIPTURE REFLECTION *(read as a group)*

> *"You search the Scriptures, for in them you think you have eternal life; and these are they which testify of Me."* – JOHN 5:39

The Old Testament records the preparation for the Christ. The Gospels record the manifestation of the Christ. The Book of Acts displays the Body of the Christ. The New Testament letters provide the explanation of the two comings of the Christ. The Book of Revelation documents the consummation of all things in Christ. Therefore the entire Bible is truly about Christ.[1]

GROUP DISCUSSION *(discuss as a group)*

01. Read 2 Timothy 3:16-17. Do you trust that all Scripture is divinely inspired? Do you believe the Bible is without error? Is there anything preventing you from allowing Scripture to be completely trustworthy and authoritative? Discuss with your group.

02. Read John 5:46 and identify and discuss three passages where Moses wrote about Christ. Hint: The Passover is one of them.

03. The Bible is 66 books written by 40 different authors over a 1,500 year period. Do these facts give your more hope or more doubt of the inerrancy of Scripture? Explain and defend your position.

"Nothing less than a whole Bible can make a whole Christian."

A.W. TOZER

Dedication & Death

INTRODUCTION *(read as a group)*

They say that when Jesus went to the cross, he owned nothing more than the clothes on his back. That's a bit different than most of us who own cars, houses, businesses, books, electronics, and more. Almost like a disease, a growing desire to own something else kindles within us. We want more. We want to keep more. We want to control more. While there is nothing inherently evil with acquiring possessions, materialism does seem to build a wall between us and Christ. If anything is clear in this chapter it's this: We cannot want anything more than Christ. We cannot place anything—even our own lives—above Christ. These are easy things to say, however, they are difficult to live.

SCRIPTURE REFLECTION *(read as a group)*

> *"For whoever desires to save his life will lose it, but whoever loses his life for My sake will find it."*
> **—MATTHEW 16:25**

Hudson Taylor once said, "Christ is either Lord of all, or He is not Lord at all." When a Christian is lukewarm it is not because he has chosen to ignore the commands of Christ, he is lukewarm because he has chosen to ignore the deity of Christ. When we truly comprehend who Christ is, correct countenance and behavior follow.

GROUP DISCUSSION *(discuss as a group)*

01. Read 1 Corinthians 6:19-20 and discuss how this truth should reorient your behavior.

02. After a Christian is born again they are a new creation who is being regenerated and transformed by the Holy Spirit. Share how God's Spirit has killed off desires of your flesh and changed your affections to the things of heaven.

03. Be honest, is there any area of your life which you have not allowed the Lord access? Does He reign in all or just most? Do you have any guilty pleasures or unhelpful habits that need to be cleared up? Unless you're perfect, drag into the light something that needs to be sanctified in your life.

"Until the will and the affections are brought under the authority of Christ, we have not begun to understand, let alone accept, His Lordship."

ELISABETH ELLIOT

Abide or Depart

INTRODUCTION *(read as a group)*

The chapter title for this session is simply another way of saying "Grow or Go." This may sound extreme but it's actually a biblical idea promoted by Jesus. Entering into a real relationship with God doesn't only require belief but regeneration, submission and obedience. In fact, without regeneration, submission, and obedience, relationship is null. God expects change. Not because it is our sole duty to manufacture change but because it is the natural result of someone indwelt by the Holy Spirit, bathed in the Holy Word, and in communion with the Holy God.

SCRIPTURE REFLECTION *(read as a group)*

> *"Jesus answered and said to him, 'If anyone loves Me, he will keep My word; and My Father will love him, and We will come to him and make Our home with him. He who does not love Me does not keep My words; and the*

word which you hear is not Mine but the Father's who
sent Me.'" — JOHN 14:23-24

This passage is a direct quote from Jesus that follows the if-then communication model. That is to say, "If you do this, then this will be the result." In this case it's, "If anyone loves Me, he will keep My word." Jesus understands that obedience and adherence to truth is the natural result of a real relationship with Him. While there are many methods to display our love for God, Jesus has identified conformity to His word as the chief example.

GROUP DISCUSSION *(discuss as a group)*

01. Read 1 John 5:3. What is John referring to when he says commandments? Is this a reference to the Ten Commandments? Is this a reference to Jesus' commandments in the New Testament? Is this a reference to the Gospel? Look up three commentaries on this verse to determine if you're seeing this in line with other theologians.

02. If we're saved by belief in Christ and not by our works, why is it important that we are obedient? Read Romans 6:1-14. Discuss with your group.

03. Do you feel that you're a victim to sin and not a victor over it? Do you feel like sin happens to you and you don't choose it? Read 1 Corinthians 10:13 and discuss with your group.

"Obedience is the only reality. It is faith visible, faith acting, and faith manifest. It is the test of real discipleship among the Lord's people."

J.C. RYLE

Do You Really Love Jesus?

INTRODUCTION *(read as a group)*

In this session, I attempted to illuminate the great divide between spiritual activity and spiritual standing. Outside of Christ, we have no hope. This is why the Gospel is so extraordinary. It's Good News because there is bad news. We are alive because we were dead. We are healed because we were sick. Our affections have been changed. Our desires have been modified. Do not think for a moment that you were the one who accomplished this great work. You have not been awakened because of your works. You have been awakened because of His work. Brothers and sisters, remember that your spiritual activity is an outpouring of your spiritual standing—not the other way around.

SCRIPTURE REFLECTION *(read as a group)*

"For by grace you have been saved through faith, and that not of yourselves; it is the gift of God, not of works, lest anyone should boast." –EPHESIANS 2:8-9

The emphasis that salvation is not anything done by you is abundantly clear. In this one passage, we get two explicitly negative statements: "not of yourselves," and "not of works." The Lord has leveled the playing field for all time. He has chosen us. He has made the way. He has bridged the gap. Lord, let us not forget our absence in the work of salvation; for it is You who declare freedom. It is simply for us to respond accordingly!

GROUP DISCUSSION *(discuss as a group)*

01. What have we been saved from? What's the bad news of the Gospel and how do you include it in the ministry of evangelism?

02. Legalism is a term tossed around the church today. What is true legalism? How can we separate the call to conform to the commands of scripture from the accusations of legalism?

03. Read Romans 3:10; 3:23 and Ephesians 2:5 and discuss the doctrines of total depravity and prevenient grace. If you're unaware of those doctrines, look them up online.

"Amazing grace! How sweet the sound that saved a wretch like me! I once was lost but now am found, was blind but now I see."

JOHN NEWTON

Costless Christianity

INTRODUCTION *(read as a group)*

Do you believe you're in a war? I'm being serious. Take a moment and ponder this question. The truth is, Scripture makes it clear that, as a Christian, you're in a spiritual war. However, most of us are too blinded by Westernized pursuits to perceive the spiritual landscape around us. If you know anyone in the American military, they will tell you that they don't see individualism like the rest of us. In fact, they feel owned by the government.

Interestingly, the Bible presents a similar idea regarding those who are saved. We were bought at a price (1 Cor. 6:19), therefore, we are to submit, serve, and yield to Christ. We are required to give up our life and realign our pursuits to His directives, objectives, and mission. It's clear, Christianity comes at a cost. You are a soldier of Jesus Christ. You, me, we have a commission—a great one at that! The question is, are you participating? Are you paying the price? Or are you AWOL?

SCRIPTURE REFLECTION *(read as a group)*

> *"And Jesus came and spoke to them, saying, 'All authority has been given to Me in heaven and on earth. Go therefore and make disciples of all the nations, baptizing them in the name of the Father and of the Son and of the Holy Spirit, teaching them to observe all things that I have commanded you; and lo, I am with you always, even to the end of the age.' Amen"*
> **—MATTHEW 28:18-20**

01. When was the last time you presented the Gospel to someone? This is different than sharing your faith. When was the last time you fulfilled the work of the Great Commission (Matt. 28:18-20)? What's preventing you for accomplishing this work more frequently? Share with your group.

02. What biblical truths are you standing for in your city, state, or country? The fierceness of the resistance is usually a telling indicator of how precious the lie is to the enemy. Discuss with your group where the war is most intense in your community.

03. Read 1 Corinthians 15:58. Has there ever been a biblical truth you should have spoken up about, but instead remained silent? What does it mean to be "steadfast and immovable" and "always abounding in the work of the Lord"?

"Truth carries with it confrontation. Truth demands confrontation: loving confrontation, but confrontation nevertheless."

FRANCIS SCHAEFFER

Eternally Secure or Relationally Contingent?

INTRODUCTION *(read as a group)*

The great debate between predestination and free-will. In A.W. Tozer's *Paths to Power* he writes, "God cannot do our repenting for us. In our efforts to magnify grace we have so preached the truth as to convey the impression that repentance is a work of God. This is a grave mistake, and one which is taking a frightful toll among Christians everywhere. God has commanded all men to repent. It is a work which only they can do."[2] This statement supports my argument in this chapter that our relationship with God was not decided for us, we chose it through belief and repentance. In other words, as Christians, God works in us but He does so in a co-operating format. While He is sovereign, He does not violate our free-will. While He is all powerful, He does not force us to obey. Instead, He woos us and leads us as a loving shepherd does with his sheep. It is upon this foundation of relationship that we can properly understand *our* role in this divine dance.

SCRIPTURE REFLECTION *(read as a group)*

> *"Therefore, my beloved, as you have always obeyed, not as in my presence only, but now much more in my absence, work out your own salvation with fear and trembling; for it is God who works in you both to will and to do for His good pleasure."*
> **—PHILIPPIANS 2:2-13**

My aim for this session is simple: How does our relationship with God operate? What role do we play? What role does God play? In the passage above, we have two truths, two truths that sit side-by-side, seemingly irreconcilable and yet both undeniable. We get to "work out our own salvation with fear and trembling" (our responsibility) and "God works in us to both will and to do for His good pleasure" (His responsibility). This teaches us two things: First, even though God is sovereign, we have spiritual responsibility and free-will. Second, somehow God works in us, without violating our free-will, to accomplish His will and work in us and through us.

GROUP DISCUSSION *(discuss as a group)*

01.   How do you view your relationship with God? What are your responsibilities? What would happen to your relationship if you stopped fulfilling these duties?

02.   If we maintain relationship with God, what does He promise to deliver? Consider Philippians 1:6 and 1 Peter 1:5, 2 Peter 1:10, 2 Timothy 4:18, and Jude 1:24.

"Some people think God does not like to be troubled with a relationship filled with constant coming and asking. But the way to trouble God is not to come at all."

D.L. MOODY

Hate the Captor, Not the Captive

INTRODUCTION *(read as a group)*

From a distance, it's easy to blame God for the evil in our world. But the truth is, God did not create evil. He simply created a world in which evil could exist. Why? Without the possibility of evil we cannot have good. Without the possibility of hate we cannot have love. God did not author evil but had to allow for its possibility in order for true love and true goodness to exist. Without the alternative of love, love is not love—it is neutral.

In other words, without the existence of the Tree of the Knowedge of Good and Evil in the Garden of Eden, love could not have existed. God had to offer a way for humanity to **not** choose Him in order for true love to be present. However, by temptation of the enemy, we did not choose Him. We chose ourselves, and as a result, sin entered into the world (Romans 5:12). God is not to blame for the pain, suffering, and death in our world. It is the enemy, it is our flesh, and it is the disease of sin.

SCRIPTURE REFLECTION *(read as a group)*

"For if you forgive men their trespasses, your heavenly Father will also forgive you. But if you do not forgive men their trespasses, neither will your Father forgive your trespasses."
—MATTHEW 6:14-15

In a world with sin, we get hurt. People hurt us. Christians hurt us. Our parents hurt us. Even our pastors hurt us. Although these individuals are called to take responsibility for their actions through repentance, we are still left with the duty of forgiveness and grace and mercy. We are called to empathize with the fallen state of our brothers and sisters and forgive them their trespasses as our father in heaven has forgiven ours. But most of all, we are to attribute the pain of sin to the activator of sin. While God has allowed sin to magnify His glory, He has not approved of sin. When we think correctly about the matter of sin we can properly place fault to its rightful composer.

GROUP DISCUSSION *(discuss as a group)*

01. What happens if you refuse to forgive others? How many unforgiven people are in heaven? Discuss with your group.

02. Read Luke 6:27-28. Does this verse mean we are to be total pacifists? How can we be obedient to this verse while standing for truth and upholding God's justice?

03. Read Proverbs 8:13. What's the difference between hating evil and hating the people who commit evil? Discuss.

"Our forgiving others is not a cause of God's forgiving us, but it is a condition without which He will not forgive us."

THOMAS WATSON

Share the Blessing of Real Christianity

"Behold, how good and how pleasant it is for brethren to dwell together in unity!" **—PSALM 133:1**

You've finished the *Real Christianity Study Guide*! I hope it has brought you into a deeper understanding of your Lord. As I wrote in the *Real Christianity* conclusion, the safest and most joyful place we will ever be is connected with a local church, under the instruction of Jesus Christ and His Word. It is here that God's children can and should expect to experience God at His fullest. It is here where God's people can be united under His Kingship. It is here where *real* Christianity is birthed, nurtured, grown, tested, matured, and perfected until the Day of our Lord returns.

If you're not an active, participating member of a Bible-based local church please make that a priority. If you're looking to better understand what a biblical church should look like, we have a variety of articles, podcast, and resources available for you at RelearnChurch.org.

Lastly, can I ask a favor? Would you consider sharing the blessing of *Real Christianity* and this study guide with your friends and family? Tell them to use the coupon code **FRIENDS&FAMILY** at Shop.RelearnChurch.org to get 10% off their purchase.

May God continue to bless you with His truth,

Dale Partridge

Endnotes

1 Adaptation of content from: https://www.blueletterbible.org/faq/don_stewart/don_stewart_204.cfm

2 Paths to power – A. W. Tozer – Chapter 2 – God's Part and Man's

NOTES

Made in the USA
Lexington, KY
05 December 2019

57996680R00035